The Pain in the Chest

by Áine Murray

This Book Belongs to:

_ _

ISBN: 978-1-913275-34-1

Illustration & Design: Bronagh Lee

This book was published in cooperation with Choice Publishing, Drogheda, Co. Louth, Republic of Ireland.

www.choicepublishing.ie

When I was just five
I saw a balloon
And it shone with the face
of my favourite cartoon

weeeeeeeeeeeeee
Popcorn

It was floating away
On a thin silver string

So I reached out my hand
To grab hold of the thing

But...
What if I took it
And it popped in my ears?
What if the string
hurt my hand and
brought me to tears?
What if another child
Saw it as well
And pushed me so hard
To get it, that I fell?

And I couldn't quite reach
Without leaving my mum

And if I lost her
What would I have done?

So my hand fell back down
At my side to rest
corn dogs
And I walked away
With a Pain In My Chest

When I was just seven
My school did a show

And I longed and I longed
To play the hero

I knew every line
I had learned them by heart
I would surely be
The best kid for the part.

But...

I thought of the stage
And I thought of the crowd

What if they all thought
My voice was too loud ?

What if I slipped
Or I mess up the song?
And the teacher gets angry
And says that I'm wrong
And a lot of other
Kids wanted the lead.
If I got the part
They'd hate me, indeed.
LINES
WORLD MAP
So though I learned the lines
Just like all the rest
I didn't try out
With a Pain In My Chest.

When I was just twelve
Starting Secondary School
I put on my new shoes
And I looked really cool

As everyone walked
Groups of fours,

threes and twos...

I noticed a girl
Who was wearing my shoes.

She was quiet and stylish
And alone just like me
And I wanted to meet her
And be friends, maybe.

But...

I started to think
She must like to sit alone

Her face is looking
Right down at her phone.

And she'd probably be
Embarrassed and mad
That we had the same shoes
That's not funny, it's sad

And I bet she's just waiting
For all her friends, so
I'd just be annoying
If I said hello.

So I walked away
Not feeling the best.
A little bit lonely

With a Pain In My Chest.

I was nearly 18
Just before my birth date
And I wanted a party
To celebrate.

When I asked my mum
She looked at me, bemused

"You want a big party?
I'm a little confused."
TEA
SUGAR
"You've always hated being
At the centre of the room
You hate meeting people
You even hate balloons!"
S
P

“If you don’t want a party
You just have to say

Don’t just do it
Because it’s your birthday.”

“I think they’re the best
But I’ve always been stopped
By the Pain In My Chest.”

"Whenever I try
It stops me in my track
Whenever I hope
It decides to attack."

Even as I spoke
Much to my surprise
Came the Pain In My Chest
And tears in my eyes...

“Oh my dear, I know well
The Pain In Your Chest
It happens to me too
When I’m anxious and stressed”

“It’s hard and upsetting
And it’s strong and it’s bad
But now that you’ve told me
I’m ever so glad”

The pain in your chest is called

“And it’s hard to battle
But you can trust me”

“The thing that anxiety
Hates the most
Is when we share it
With all who are close.”

"Because when we talk
And when we share
Our friends can support us
They can learn how to care.

So if you try but you can't
You must let them know
That sometimes you're anxious
Although it may not show"

And the more we talk
Saying loud and far
That the pain in your chest
Is not who you are

More people will learn

More people will care

Maybe others will realise

Maybe others will share

Share their panic
and sadness
and upset
and distress

And together we'll slowly
Cure the Pain In The Chest.

The End